This book is dedicated to my children – Branden, Chris and Julia – who have been my wisest teachers when it comes to love, and sharing, and celebrating what is important.

Wild Whispers

Written by Theo Maehr

Illustrated by Sonja Lokensgard

Wishing you endless Wild Whispers! ♡

Theo

If fun is something
you want to have,
then listen to this story
about me and my dad.

When I was a lad
no bigger than you,
he took me to wild places
for more than the view.

As we wandered all over
the land and the sea,
Dad shared some
enlightening words with me.

These are the words
I remember so well,
"All things in this world
have a story to tell."

He finished, but continued with
a word of advice,

" If wise is something
you want to be,
listen to those stories
and become wise like me."

Not having much money
right then you see,
the best thing of all, was
those whispers were free.

So I listened, and
though I am not one to boast,
I think those wild whispers
have taught me the most.

Just remember that
when you finish this book,
there are endless wild whispers
in all places you look.

Some whispers I'll share
in the next few pages,
and if you hear for yourself,
you'll be as wise as the sages.

From the mountains I learned
to find stillness within.

There's a refuge inside —
far away from the din.

The oak taught me
that firm I could stand,
and the willow, that
sometimes it's better to bend.

The wind brought me whispers
of things far and near,
better yet when I listened
with more than my ears.

Chickadees called,
" Remember good cheer!"

For even on the coldest
and grayest of days,
they flit, peep and cheep
in the merriest ways.

Deer warned me sometimes
to jump high and clear,
and always be ready,
awake and aware.

I learned from horse
to take joy in a run.

Running fast
can be a whole lot of fun.

And I learned by watching
the ants and the bees
the importance
of working harmoniously.

Those tiny insects
can accomplish great deeds,
together fulfilling
the colony's needs.

Patience I learned
from the owl and hawk,
who wait hours for meals
with nary a squawk.

Dog taught me to use
my sense of smell,
for the smells in this world
have their story to tell

I learned from streams
to finish tasks once begun,
and not to give up
when things are not fun.

Over obstacles and blocks,
around boulders and trees,
as rapids and waterfalls,
streams flow to the sea.

Fox taught me to walk
with barely a sound,
as I watched, looked, and listened
while wandering around.

The wild creatures hide
when they hear people come,
so I learned to walk quietly —
called the "foxwalk" by some.

No matter its name,
it's a skill you could learn —
you'll see more in the wilds
at each bend and turn.

Dandelion
is a plant I love.
All parts can be eaten,
below ground and above.

The roots make a wonderful
tonic and tea,
while young leaves gently steamed
taste good to me.

When exploring the woods,
just out on a hack,
dandelion blossoms
make a wonderful snack.

Dandelion gives
all of itself,
to any person or animal
that needs it for health.

So next time you see
this plant known as a weed,
you might thank it
for fulfilling so many needs.

At our own cozy home,
where the soil was like loam,

we gardened a lot
as the weather grew hot.

We pulled up the weeds,
and planted handfuls of seeds.

The whisper I heard
from those seeds large and small,
was " Believe in me
and I'll grow, you'll see!"

They gave us great meals
with such lively fresh tastes,
that to eat anything else
seemed almost a waste.

So every year in the spring
I plant all kinds of things.

In beautiful rows
or from vigorous throws,
my garden blossoms and grows.

And when the plants grow old,
 I don't whack them with a hoe.

Instead I thank them
and leave them alone.

In return they make seeds
that look like small stones.

Then I am back with those seeds
in the spring,
out in the dirt
doing the gardening thing.

I won't end here concerning edible fare.
Across the land, almost everywhere,
the wild plants whisper that they are there.

They give nourishment and health,
gifts much greater than wealth,
to anyone who will learn
to carefully discern,
which plants at their feet
they can pick up and eat.

Eating's an adventure
when you're out and about —
as you find wild food growing
you'll just want to shout!

The sun shares a whisper
that is quite grand to hear,
though it is something to realize,
not sense with the ear.

The whisper comes
from above — up high —
as the sun crosses
the wide blue sky.

It shines its bright rays on
all things just the same,
no matter their look,
no matter their name.

No matter what gifts
to earth they bring,
it doesn't matter
if they can sing.

No matter if they have
four feet or two wings,
no matter if they have flippers,
webbed feet or fins.

No matter if they are
rooted to the ground,
the sun shares its light
without even a sound.

Never asking a return
for this life-giving gift,
if only each other
we could equally uplift.

Though more pages I could fill
with more whispers from the wilds,

When you start hearing your own,
you'll be wearing a smile.

There is one last whisper
I'll again repeat,
so the point of this story
stays nice and neat.

As we think of these lessons
so amazingly clear,
Dad's own wild whisper
is always quite near,

"All things have a story
if you take time to hear."

A Message from Theo Maehr

20 years ago I was in New Hampshire in the late spring helping to build a house. At the end of my time there, I ventured north to the White Mountains to hike my favorite loop trail up Mount Lafayette.

I arrived on a beautifully clear day with few clouds in the sky. I made the summit of Mount Lafayette after many hours of climbing, found a sheltered place out of the wind amongst the rocks and settled down to eat my lunch. As I gazed out over the beautiful landscape before me I received a very clear message from the mountain, "if you wish to know silence, remember me."

I was surprised, excited and quieted all in the same moment. I saw the vibrancy of the world around me and felt at one with it. I felt no desire to eat, but instead basked in the magnitude and profound quality of the experience.

Eventually, I continued on my way over to Mount Lincoln and down a snowy trail toward the bottom.

During the rest of my day in the mountains I experienced a heightened awareness of and connection with my surroundings. I received quiet whispers from a stream, a chickadee and a grove of birch as I descended. I felt very childlike and playful as I hiked along.

As a result of the experiences of the day, I felt inspired to begin a children's book called Wild Whispers, about the messages we can receive from the world around us if we are quiet enough to listen and hear. Though inspired, I was so busy with my work building houses that I did not take the time to write.

Finally, on one fateful day I injured my thumb with a circular saw and I had to stop working for a number of weeks. It was during that recovery time that I finally wrote Wild Whispers.

Writing the story was a unifying experience. In the process I relived my hike up the mountains and tuned in to other messages from the wild world.

About the Author

Theo Maehr is a teacher and artist who has lived in Big Sur for more than twenty years.

In addition to being an author Theo is a lyre maker, ship captain, farmer, photographer, house builder, and diver.

His prior endeavors include Waldorf teaching, professional storytelling, outdoor education, agriculture, construction, raft guiding, and lots and lots of wandering around in nature.

Theo currently lives in the Santa Lucia mountains of Big Sur, California, where he has built himself a delightfully sturdy off-the-grid home with an ample garden and orchard.

About the Illustrator

Sonja Lokensgard is a visionary artist, illustrator, yoga teacher, singer and lover of life. She travels worldwide to share her gifts of art, movement, meditation and music.

Sonja, who resides in Virginia, finds joy in the moment through teaching yoga, painting, and hospice volunteering, as well as a healthy dose of hoop dancing to live music.

With deep gratitude for the wild whispers of nature, Sonja hopes to continue offering her paintings as a way for both adults and children to connect in loving relationship with one another and the earth.

Wild Whispers

ISBN: 978-0-9967802-4-7 *paperbound*

ISBN: 978-0-9967802-5-4 *hardbound*

Designed and Published by
Lucky Valley Press
Jacksonville, Oregon
www.LuckyValleyPress.com

Printed in the United States of America on paper that meets
the Sustainable Forestry Initiative® Chain-of-Custody Standards.
WWW.SFIPROGRAM.ORG

CPSIA information can be obtained
at www.ICGtesting.com
Printed in the USA
LVHW05s0805190418
574041LV00004B/5/P

9 780996 780247